Worship So

and Hymns

for Every Choir

# BLENDED PRAISE

Arranged in 10 Medleys by

## TOM FETTKE

## PRODUCTS AVAILABLE:

Choral Book.........................................0-6330-9693-8

Listening CD.......................................0-6330-9694-6

Listening Cassette...............................0-6330-9696-2

Accompaniment CD...........................0-6330-9697-0
(Split Track and Instruments Only)

CD Promo Pak....................................0-6330-9699-7

Cassette Promo Pak...........................0-6330-9698-9

CD Kit.................................................0-6330-9707-1
(10 Choral Books, Listening CD, and Accompaniment CDs)

GENEVOX

# FOREWORD

LifeWay Church Resources has a long-standing commitment to provide practical ministry tools to all churches. I was blessed to join their creative and editorial teams to bring you *Blended Praise*. The term *blended* best describes this collection because 10 of the most-loved praise and worship songs are joined with 10 traditional gospel hymn favorites. We worked to keep vocal ranges accessible, an important aspect in the *You Can!* Music Series. The difficulty levels of the parts are not extreme, and you will be thoroughly pleased with the track quality. These medleys are versatile and heartwarming and may be sung by any size choir or worship ministry.

To God be the glory as you, your choir, and music ministry teams unite your voices in *Blended Praise*!

Tom Fettke

# CONTENTS

# PRODUCTION NOTES

Two CD options are provided with *Blended Praise:* the split track (with voices) is on Disc 1; the stereo track (instruments only) is on Disc 2. On the split track, voices are on the right channel, and instruments are on the left channel. On the stereo track, instruments are on both channels with no voices.

These CDs contain rehearsal point designations that correspond with CD points provided throughout each song in the choral book. CD points in the choral book are indicated by a box containing a number and are identical for both discs. These numbers provide points of reference to help you locate that section on the CD.

## BASS CLEF OPTION

*Blended Praise* offers the bass clef feature, a requested option in the *You Can!* Music Series. This part is included for male choir members who are familiar with reading bass clef. This feature expands the options, but it does not increase difficulty. Most often the bass clef is a duplication of the treble clef notes, so the men may read either staff. The entire collection may be sung in unison.

## GLOSSARY OF MUSIC TERMS

Various terms are used throughout the music to guide the singers and director in the musical performance. Many of these terms are Italian. Here is a partial listing:

| | | |
|---|---|---|
| *rit.* | *ritardando*—gradually slowing | |
| *a tempo* | returning to the original tempo (speed of music) | |
| *dim.* | *diminuendo*—gradually getting softer | |
| *cresc.* | *crescendo*—gradually getting louder | |
| *unis.* | unison—everyone sings melody (no harmony parts) | |
| *div.* | *divisi*—dividing into more than one part (melody and harmony) | |

# Lift Up Your Heads
*with*
# When We All Get to Heaven

*Arranged by Tom Fettke*

*CD rehearsal points for Split-track and Stereo track products are identical.

† "Lift Up Your Heads." Words and music by STEVE FRY.

# In the Presence of Jehovah
*with*
# Like a River Glorious

*Arranged by Tom Fettke*

Troubles vanish, hearts are mended, in the presence of the King.

† "Like a River Glorious"

LADIES unis.

Like a river glorious

a little faster

† "Like a River Glorious." Words by FRANCES R. HAVERGAL. Music by JAMES MOUNTAIN.

# Praise the Name of Jesus
*with*
# Glorious Is Thy Name

*Arranged by Tom Fettke*

† "Praise the Name of Jesus"
CHOIR unis.

Praise the name of Je - sus! Praise the name of Je - sus!

He's my Rock, He's my For - tress, He's my De - liv - er - er; in

† "Glorious Is Thy Name"

Glo-rious is Thy name, O Lord! name, O

Lord! Great Re-deem-er,

Lord and Mas-ter, Light of all e-ter-nal days;

# Here I Am to Worship
*with*
# O Worship the King

*Arranged by Tom Fettke*

wor - ship, here I am to bow down, Here I am to say that You're my God.

\_ You're al - to - geth - er love - ly, al - to - geth - er

wor - thy, Al - to - geth - er won - der - ful to me.\_ Here I am to

# O Lord, You're Beautiful
*with*
# Beautiful Savior

*Arranged by Tom Fettke*

† "O Lord, You're Beautiful"

1st time: SOLO (or LADIES unis.)     2nd time: CHOIR unis.

soul,    my  joy,  my  crown.

an - gels  in  the

sky.

Beau - ti - ful  Sav - ior,  Lord  of  the

# He Is Exalted
*with*
# Praise Him! Praise Him!

*Arranged by Tom Fettke*

† "He Is Exalted." Words and music by TWILA PARIS.
© Copyright 1985 and this arrangement © copyright 2003 Straightway Music/Mountain Spring Music/ASCAP
(all rights administered by EMI Christian MusicPublishing). All rights reserved. Used by permission.

54

# My Tribute
*with*
# To God Be the Glory

*Arranged by Tom Fettke*

† "My Tribute"

To God be the glo - ry, To God be the glo - ry! To God be the

# Bless His Holy Name
*with*
# Blessed Be the Name

*Arranged by Tom Fettke*

† "Bless His Holy Name"

Bless the Lord, O my soul, and
all that is with-in me, Bless His ho -

# Oh, I Want to Know You More
*with*
# More About Jesus

*Arranged by Tom Fettke*

† "Oh, I Want to Know You More"

† "More About Jesus"

† "More About Jesus." Words by ELIZA E. HEWITT. Music by JOHN R. SWENEY.

breath to know You in Your death and res - ur - rec - tion.

Oh, I want to know You more. Oh, I want to know You;

Oh, I want to know You more.

# All Heav'n Declares
*with*
# Alleluia! Alleluia!

*Arranged by Tom Fettk*

82

For the__ world's sal - va - tion bled,   Je - sus Christ, the
For the__ great Re - deem - er's love;   Joy - ous songs to

King of Glo - ry,   Now is ris - en from the dead.
Him be rais - ing   Un - to God in

heav'n a - bove.

(to meas. 29)